BoB
the big BAD BLUEFISH

to Ms. Glover

Good Luck Fishing!

Bernadette Gesser
Illustrated by Sarah Grangier

Bernadette Gesser
12/3/16

For my husband, Ed,
who warned me that bluefish bite!

ISBN 978-0983075-00-4
LCCN 2010938748

PUBLISHED BY SUNSET PRESS, LLC
P.O. BOX 66
Deal Island, MD 21821
www.Sunset-Press.com

Printed in the United States of America

One bright sunny day, Fisherman Fred took his little white and green boat out into the bay to go fishing. He dug up some big fresh worms from his wife's garden to use as bait.

Fisherman Fred hoped to be lucky enough to catch some spot, croaker or even rockfish for dinner.

Spot

Spot is a type of fish called Norfolk spot. These fish swim in huge schools all around bays and rivers. They are called spot because they have a big black spot just behind their gills.

Croaker and his kind of fish got the name because of the croaking noises made when they get caught. Some people call this type of fish "hard-head" because their heads are so big and hard.

Croaker

Rocky

Rocky is a striped bass or rockfish. His type of fish is considered to be the prize fish because its meat is so tasty. Rockfish are fun to catch because they give fishermen a good fight before they are caught.

Spot, Croaker and Rocky are good friends who love to share adventures. They meet at the sand bar to play. It is the same sand bar where Fisherman Fred is going to anchor his boat.

As soon as his boat came into view, they knew how they were going to play that day. Rocky, Croaker and Spot swam around, teasing Fred by nibbling at the fresh worm on his hook.

The fish were having lots of fun and enjoyed some tasty worm snacks. Spot tugged on the line just enough to nibble the worm and Fisherman Fred would have to reel in his line and bait it again.

Fisherman Fred said, "These fish are getting too much of my bait." He started the motor on his boat and moved to a different location, just on the edge of a big hole. He didn't know that the three fish friends were watching the shadows of the boat skimming across the water and they could swim as fast as his motor would take his boat.

While swimming over to the boat, Spot looked down to see two big eyes looking straight up at him! He didn't see anything else and he became very curious as to what was watching him. He swam down to the bottom to investigate and his pals turned around and followed him. They swam past the big eyes below them two times before Rocky noticed it was a fish, hidden by the sand and seaweed on the bottom. He told Spot and Croaker that the eyes belong to a type of fish called a flounder.

Rocky explained that flounder were big, flat, lazy fish and usually wouldn't move off the bottom unless the fisherman dropped his bait right on top of them. Spot got just a little frightened. Rocky told Spot that unless he was hurt, the flounder would probably not bother him.

Some flounder live in parts of the bay that are very sandy, so they are brown with spots on one side and white on the bottom. Others live where there is a lot of sea weed or sea grass and they are green with spots on one side and white on the bottom. Their colors help them hide on the bottom, sort of like being camouflaged.

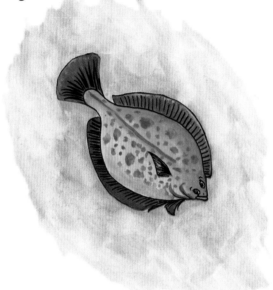

It's harder for flounder to swim as fast as some of the other fish because of their flat, oval shape. They have very soft jaws. When flounder are caught, fishermen will bring the fish up to the side of the boat but will put them in a net before lifting them in the boat. That way, they don't tear their mouths and if they are too small, the fish can be gently returned to the water.

This flounder just laid there and watched as the three friends started teasing Fisherman Fred again, taking bits of his fresh bait. They giggled each time some of the tasty worm came off the hook. After a while, the flounder got up off the bottom and swam sideways over to Rocky, Croaker and Spot.

The flounder said "Hi, my name is Flo and I'd like to be your friend." Flo joined Rocky, Croaker and Spot in the game of tug of war with the fisherman for his bait. Flo was not used to tugging the hook and just getting a little piece of the bait.

She usually chomped down on the entire bait swimming away with it! They told her how they are just taking nibbles so as not to be caught on the hook. Rocky grabbed the freshly baited hook just as the fisherman splashed it in the water. He showed Flo how to pull off tiny sections of the fresh worm.

Flo told her new friends to be careful because sometimes the fisherman will put a plastic worm on his line that has hooks hidden in it. If one of the hooks gets stuck in their jaws, they would not be able to spit it out and Fred would catch them!

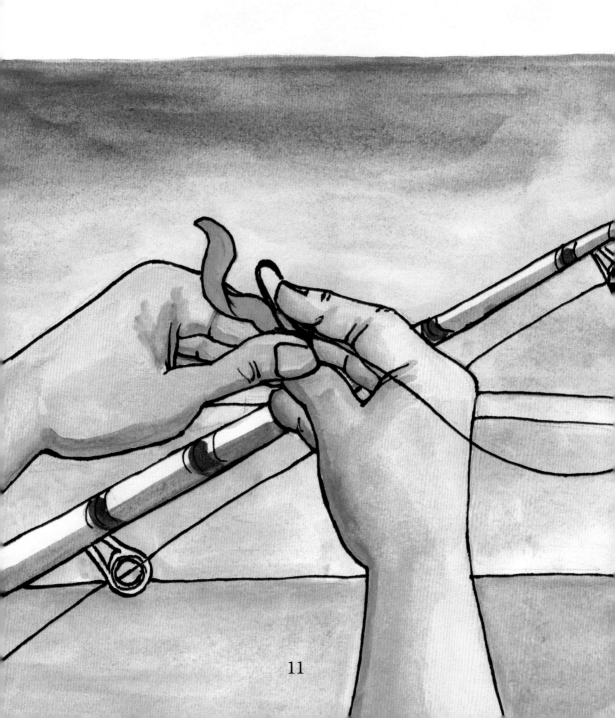

Flo explained "We're on the edge of a deep hole. We've got to be watching for Bob the Big, Bad Bluefish who hangs out near the bottom of this hole." She said that Bob was a very fast swimmer. He could dart around crab pots and in between bay grasses so fast that you would never see him coming. He was always hungry. He would bite "anything" that swims past him. He has very sharp teeth!

Bob, the Big, Bad Bluefish will eat any kind of fish that is smaller than him, especially Spot and sometimes Croakers. Bluefish can bite a line or a hook in half to get away! Bob can also chase whole schools of the smaller bait fish, making them jump out of the water to escape his massive jaws.

13

After Flo finished telling the others of the dangers of Bob, everyone started taking turns stealing Fisherman Fred's bait. Flo liked to tug the hook just as Fred was reeling it back in. She is much bigger than the others so she took big pieces of the bait. It doesn't take long for the fish to eat just about all of the fisherman's worms.

Finally, Fisherman Fred has enough of the teasing! He tries one of the green plastic jigs that looks like a worm but has a big hook hidden in it.

This is the type of lure that Flo had warned her new friends about! After all, Fisherman Fred wanted a fish for his dinner! He pulled up his anchor so his boat was just drifting over the edge of the hole with the tide. When he cast his line and it sank to the bottom, the jig started bouncing on the bay floor.

Flo saw its  bright green color and immediately called out to her friends, "Watch out! Let it go because it's not real bait!" They all moved back away from Fisherman Fred's pretty new green lure and began to head away from the boat. Out of nowhere Bob the Big, Bad Bluefish came swimming past them as fast as he could to try to get it. He chomped down so hard on the lure, he bit in half without getting any of the hook in his mouth!

Spot and Croaker became frightened when they saw his big teeth. They scampered to hide behind Flo because she was so wide. Rocky tried to steer Bob away from them by swimming very fast in front of the bluefish. Flo slowly swam over to a big patch of seaweed to hide Spot and Croaker. She sank to the bottom and almost disappeared into her surroundings. Rocky then swam into the seaweed to hide with Croaker and Spot.

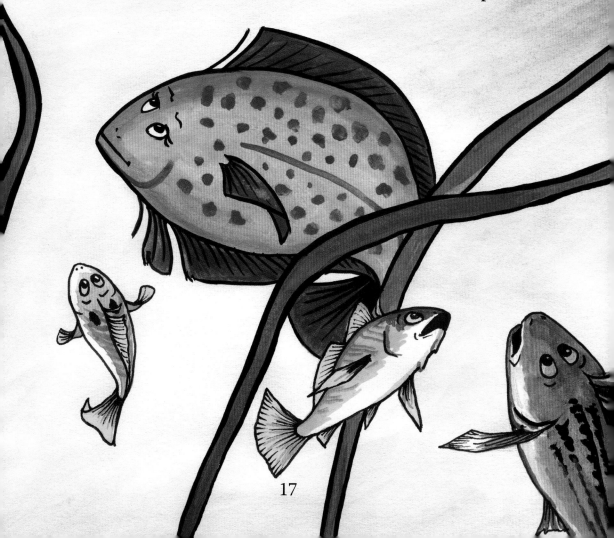

Fred felt a powerful tug on his line. He jerked the line and reeled it in only to see that half of his new green plastic lure was gone! He knew that it had to be a bluefish if his jig had been bitten in half! He rigged up a larger plastic jig and dropped it in the water, hoping that it would catch the fish he wanted for supper. Bob the Bluefish heard the splash and again, he raced over to grab at the bigger bait.

This time, Fred was able to yank his line and Bob was hooked! Fisherman Fred was reeling Bob in as fast as he could while Bob was swimming in the opposite direction to get away. The fisherman was pulling so hard that once, he lifted Bob out of the water and he made a gigantic splash. Bob was swimming so fast that he was pulling the little white and green boat. It's a real battle between man and fish!

Fisherman Fred finally got the bluefish in his boat and was holding Bob, trying to get the hook from his mouth. The hook was made so that if you turned it in a circle, you could remove it without hurting the fish. Fisherman Fred was turning the hook and just as he got it loose, Bob twisted his head around and he took a big bite of Fred's finger!

Fisherman Fred let out a loud "**YELP!**" He jumped up and grabbed his hand, letting go of Bob the Big, Bad Bluefish. Wiggling just the right way, Bob flew back into the water, creating another big splash.

The boat was really rocking so Fisherman Fred lost his balance and fell head first into the bay!

With his life preserver to help him, Fisherman Fred swam toward his boat. He tried to pull himself into the boat but the sides were too high. As Fred held onto the side, he worried that if he pulled it down too far, the boat would tip over as he tried to climb in.

Flo, Rocky, Spot and Croaker were laughing so hard they didn't see that Bob was swimming right up behind them.

By the time Croaker saw him coming, he could only yell out to the others "Be careful." Rocky swam in front of Spot to protect him and told Bob to leave his friends alone.

Bob said "I'm not going to hurt Spot. I'm just watching the fisherman trying to get back into his boat."

Fisherman Fred tried to climb over the side but when he got his leg half way over the edge of the boat, a big wave hit the boat and turned it upside down, tossing him back in the water! His fishing rod, tackle box, net and all of the rest of his bait fell to the bottom of the bay. All of the fish laughed. They thought the fisherman looked so silly trying to upright the boat. Fred was having a terrible time but with one very strong push, he was finally able to do it .

Fred swam down to the bottom to get his fishing rod, and brought it up to the boat. He hung on the side of the boat to catch his breath before he swam down again to get his tackle box and net. He didn't bother to swim back down for the rest of his bait.

This time, when he lifted his leg up over the side, he was able to hang on and he twisted to get the rest of his body back into the boat. Fred started fussing and talking to himself. Rocky heard him say, "That doggone bluefish bit me good and got me all wet! I'll come back and catch him another day." Fisherman Fred started his motor and headed home without catching any fish.

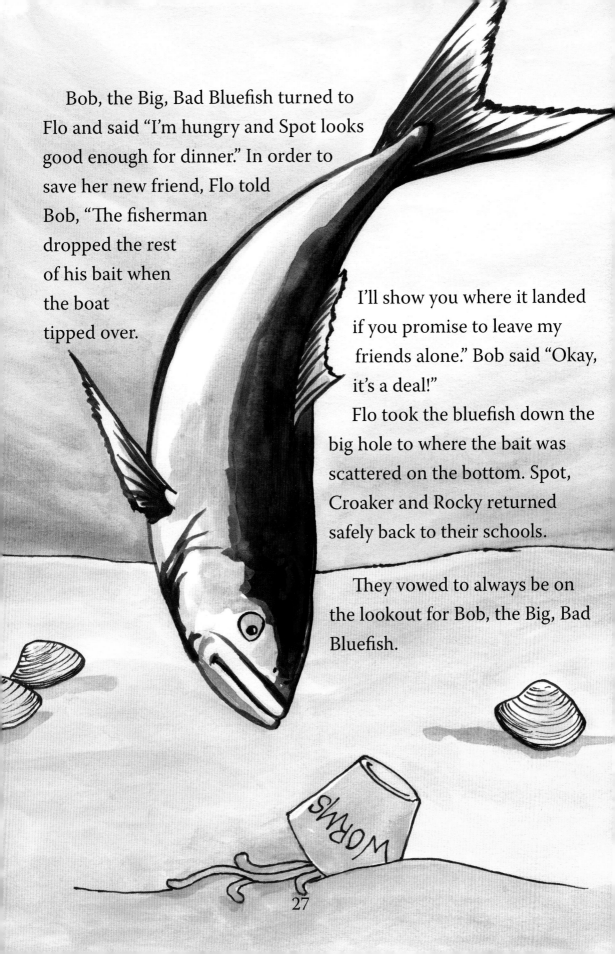

Bob, the Big, Bad Bluefish turned to Flo and said "I'm hungry and Spot looks good enough for dinner." In order to save her new friend, Flo told Bob, "The fisherman dropped the rest of his bait when the boat tipped over.

I'll show you where it landed if you promise to leave my friends alone." Bob said "Okay, it's a deal!"

Flo took the bluefish down the big hole to where the bait was scattered on the bottom. Spot, Croaker and Rocky returned safely back to their schools.

They vowed to always be on the lookout for Bob, the Big, Bad Bluefish.

About the Author

Bernadette Gesser enjoys and truly appreciates the beauty and surroundings of the Chesapeake Bay. As a young child, she learned to crab and fish from her dad by using hand lines, as he did as a child growing up on Smith Island. She is passing on the tradition by teaching her grandchildren the same fishing and crabbing techniques. She hopes that they, too, will come to appreciate and love the great beauty and bounty of the Chesapeake Bay. She is an avid "fisherman" and "chicken-necker." Family and friends look forward to her seafood feasts.

Bernadette's paternal grandfather was the last civilian keeper of the 154-year-old Seven Foot Knoll Lighthouse, which now sits on Pier 5 in Baltimore's Inner Harbor. During a ferocious storm in August 1933, he rescued six men from the tug *Point Breeze*, which sank near the lighthouse. Bernadette is currently writing a book detailing her grandfather's heroic actions and her family's contribution to the restoration of the historic lighthouse.

About the Illustrator

Sarah Watson Grangier, 29, is a professional wildlife artist from Princess Anne, Maryland. Sarah's love of nature and wildlife inspired her to capture the beautiful world around her in paintings and illustrations. She graduated with honors and a Bachelor's Degree in Art, in May of 2003 from Salisbury University.

Sarah has endured many accomplishments with her artistic talent. In addition to this book, she recently illustrated Bill Kendle's cookbook, *Healthy Eating Made Easy*. Other artistic honors include 2003 Best of Show in the Ward World Wildlife Painting Competition and 2007 Artist of the Year for the Pocomoke River Chapter Ducks Unlimited. Sarah has exhibited artwork at the Ward Museum of Wildfowl Art, the Somerset County Arts Council, the Chincoteague National Wildlife Refuge Visitor Center, the Maryland State House in Annapolis, the National Postal Museum in Washington, DC, and at the Patuxent National Wildlife Research Visitor Center where, in 2005, she was Artist of the Month for November and December.

Currently, Sarah's artwork is available online through FineArtAmerica.com, at the Flying Fish Gallery in Chincoteague, VA, the Whitehaven Hotel in Whitehaven, MD, and through the Art Institute and Gallery in Salisbury, MD.

Sunset Press, LLC

P.O. BOX 66
DEAL ISLAND, MD 21821
410-784-2310

ORDERING INFORMATION

DESCRIPTION	QTY	PRICE	TOTAL
Bob, the Big Bad Bluefish		$12.95	
TOTAL			
Shipping for 1 to 3 books			$4.95
Maryland Residents add 6% sales tax			
TOTAL ENCLOSED			

SHIP TO	
STREET	
CITY/STATE/ZIP	

Make check payable to Sunset Press, LLC

Do yourself a favor— Take a kid fishing!

30